Gruesome Grammar

Louis Fidge

In a hidden cave, far away in a magical land, lives a wise wizard, called Whimstaff. Every now and again, he searches for a young apprentice, so he can pass on his magical English powers. And this time, Whimstaff has chosen you!

Whimstaff shares the cave with a goblin and a little, red dragon. Pointy, the goblin, is very clever. The dragon, called Miss Snufflebeam, breathes small puffs of fire. She is clumsy and often loses the wizard's magical letters and numbers.

Pointy has two greedy, pet frogs, called Mugly and Bugly, who are very lazy and spend most of their time croaking, eating and sleeping. But every so often, they amaze Pointy by helping with an exercise!

Wizard Whimstaff and his friends are very happy in their cave, solving English problems. Join them on a magical quest to become a fully qualified English wizard!

Contents

Startling Standard English

I'm Wizard Whimstaff and I'm here to help you in your quest. You need to know that standard English is the kind of language you are expected to use in school. Non-standard English is often used in everyday speech.

Me and Mugly like snoozing.

This is written in non-standard English.

Mugly and I like snoozing.

This is written in standard English.

Task 1 Have a go at this exercise. Tick ✔ the sentences that are written in standard English. Cross ✘ the sentences that are written in non-standard English.

a The wizard ain't here.

b We done it yesterday.

c Me spells was in me book.

d What yer want?

e I saw the man what done it.

f Tom and I went home.

g I would like a new wand.

h I'm going to play outside.

i That's really naughty.

j I can run faster than you.

Task 2 Do the best you can with this task! Match each non-standard English sentence with the same sentence written in standard English.

Non-standard English	Standard English
a I could of eaten it easy.	Do you want a sweet?
b I am sensibler than you.	I don't know anything about it.
c These ain't my boots.	I am more sensible than you.
d We seen him do it.	These are not my boots.
e Do you wanna sweet?	All of us were hungry.
f All of us was hungry.	I could easily have eaten it.
g I don't know nothing about it.	We saw him do it.

Task 3 Allakazan! Try and rewrite these non-standard English sentences in standard English.

a He learned me some magic tricks. _____

b Me and Dan hid in the cellar. _____

c I ain't going out. _____

d We was just stirring the cauldron. _____

e That's the spell what I made up. _____

f We coming soon. _____

g What you got there? _____

h You done it well. _____

i He should of took more care. _____

j Have you seen me broomstick? _____

k We was lucky not to get caught. _____

l Give me one of them apples. _____

Sorcerer's Skill Check

You should never use a double negative in the same sentence, if you want to become an English wizard. Write each sentence correctly.

a I'm not never doing tricks again! _____ *I'm never doing tricks again!*

b I haven't got no money. _____

c I don't want no trouble. _____

d They weren't nowhere near me. _____

e The children did not take no notice. _____

Award yourself a gold star and stick it on your
certificate on page 32, young apprentice. Super!

3

Spooky Summaries

I'm Miss Snufflebeam and I'm supposed to tell you about saying things in a shorter way, but I'm not very good at it myself! **Summarising** means shortening a piece of text without losing its meaning.

<u>Granite</u>, <u>limestone</u>, <u>marble</u> are all different types of <u>rocks</u>.

When we classify things one word may be used for several.

<u>cave</u> – a deep hollow place usually with an entrance in rock

In definitions, one word may also be used or several.

<u>PTO</u> means – please turn over.

Sometimes we use abbreviations to shorten words.

Task 1   Help! I've got these abbreviations and their meanings muddled up. Help me match up each abbreviation with its correct meaning.

a   Mr

b   Rd

c   NB

d   St

e   USA

note well (Latin: *nota bene*)

postscript

United States of America

Mister

please reply (French: *répondez s'il vous plaît*)

Road

Saint

please turn over

and so on (Latin: *et cetera*)

Great Britain

f   GB

g   PS

h   etc.

i   RSVP

j   PTO

Task 2

Dabracababra! My head hurts when I get confused! Help me write down one word which summarises each set of nouns.

Set of words	Description	Set of words	Description
a ash, oak, chestnut	trees	**f** London, Paris, Rome	
b wheat, maize, barley		**g** hammer, saw, drill	
c lion, bear, mouse		**h** tin, copper, zinc	
d cod, plaice, haddock		**i** tennis, hockey, golf	
e coat, trousers, skirt		**j** earwig, beetle, ant	

Task 3

Can you help me with this exercise? Think of one word for each definition.

a a_____ a short way of writing a word

b b_____ a kind of tall cup

c c_____ the words repeated after every verse in a poem or song

d d_____ dry land where very few plants can grow

e e_____ a female sheep

f f_____ water that shoots up into the air

Sorcerer's Skill Check

Oh no! I've got to make each pair of sentences into one shorter sentence. The wizard has done the first one for us.

a The cave was damp. It was underground. <u>The damp cave was underground.</u>

b Her sister helped her. Her sister was older. _____

c The girl was thirsty. She asked for a drink. _____

d The rain was heavy. It flooded the street. _____

e Her dress was smart. It was bright red. _____

Croak! Give yourself a gold star, you clever apprentice!

Sizzling Speech

We're Mugly and Bugly and we're here to give you a brain cell alert! Did you know that we can write speech in two ways – as direct or indirect speech? Indirect speech can also be called reported speech, because we use it to report what someone says.

The wizard said, "I can fly fast."

This is written in direct speech. The exact words spoken are inside speech marks.

The wizard said that he could fly fast.

This is written in indirect (or reported) speech. The wizard's exact words are not used, nor are speech marks. The words have been changed slightly.

Task 1 Slurp! These sentences contain direct speech. Put in the missing speech marks correctly.

a The magician chanted, Abracadabra!

b Kyle asked, What is the answer?

c Let's go out to play, suggested Paul.

d Stop shouting! the teacher ordered.

e I like your trainers, William sighed.

f It's raining outside, Shannon said.

g Tell me a story, the toddler pleaded.

h I don't like custard! Amy exclaimed.

Task 2 You look pretty clever, so try this exercise. Put in the missing speech marks in each sentence. Then write each sentence in a different way.

a The frog said, "I can hop." _____"I can hop," the frog said._____

b I'm the best at spelling, the girl boasted. _____

c I feel worn out, Dionne complained. _____

d James asked, What are you looking at? _____

e Stop it! shouted Cara. _____

f Ben asked, Have you seen my pen? _____

g Get out of my way! the lady snapped. _____

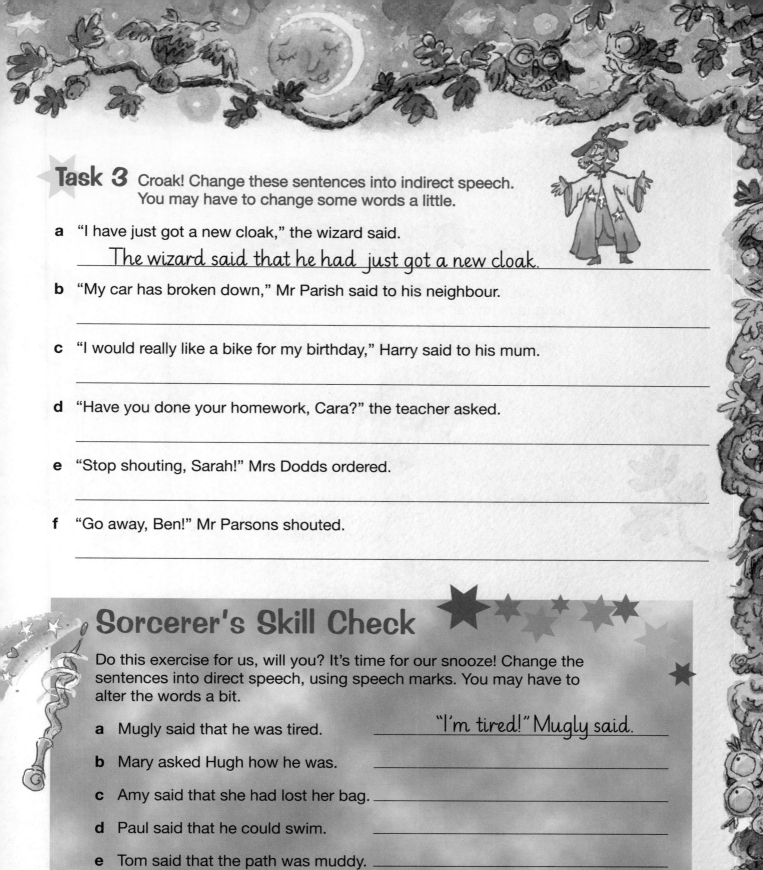

Task 3 Croak! Change these sentences into indirect speech. You may have to change some words a little.

a "I have just got a new cloak," the wizard said.

The wizard said that he had just got a new cloak.

b "My car has broken down," Mr Parish said to his neighbour.

_____

c "I would really like a bike for my birthday," Harry said to his mum.

_____

d "Have you done your homework, Cara?" the teacher asked.

_____

e "Stop shouting, Sarah!" Mrs Dodds ordered.

_____

f "Go away, Ben!" Mr Parsons shouted.

_____

Sorcerer's Skill Check

Do this exercise for us, will you? It's time for our snooze! Change the sentences into direct speech, using speech marks. You may have to alter the words a bit.

a Mugly said that he was tired.   _"I'm tired!" Mugly said._

b Mary asked Hugh how he was.   _____

c Amy said that she had lost her bag. _____

d Paul said that he could swim.   _____

e Tom said that the path was muddy. _____

f Ben asked if he could go home.   _____

Well completed, my apprentice. You deserve a gold star for your certificate!

Common Expressions

We use many common expressions in our language, my apprentice. It is time for you to learn some of them. Sometimes their meanings may be difficult to understand.

Look before you leap.

This really means: Don't rush into things. Think carefully before you make any decisions.

Task 1 Do the best you can with this exercise. Work your magic and choose a word to complete each well-known phrase.

a alive and _____

b fame and _____

c head and _____

d lock and _____

e stuff and _____

f tooth and _____

g safe and _____

h chop and _____

i flesh and _____

j high and _____

k touch and _____

l here and _____

m ways and _____

n over and _____

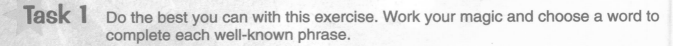

Task 2
Proverbs are wise sayings that have been around for a long time. Have a go at this exercise. Match the beginning and ending of each proverb.

a A new broom   are soon parted.

b The early bird   run deep.

c A fool and his money   catches the worm.

d No news   deserves another.

e Practice   sweeps clean.

f Still waters   makes perfect.

g One good turn   is good news.

Task 3
Allakazan! Use the magic words in the box to complete each common saying. Be quick, before they disappear!

first served	no robbery	ends well	than never	think alike	twice shy

a All's well that _____.   d Better late _____.

b Fair exchange is _____.   e First come, _____.

c Once bitten, _____.   f Great minds _____.

Sorcerer's Skill Check

Don't worry if this seems hard at first, my apprentice! In your own words, say what lesson you think we are meant to learn from each of these sayings.

a Too many cooks spoil the broth. _____

b Birds of a feather flock together. _____

c A rolling stone gathers no moss. _____

d Two heads are better than one. _____

e Empty vessels make most noise. _____

Rabracadada! You've earned another gold star!
I wish I was as clever as you!

Active and Passive Verbs

I'm Pointy and I'm here to point you in the right direction. Active and passive verbs may seem tricky at first, but they're really quite easy!

The giant <u>gnawed</u> the bone.

The bone <u>was gnawed</u> by the giant.

A verb is active when the subject of the sentence performs the action.

A verb is passive when the subject of the sentence has the action done to it.

Task 1 You'll soon get the hang of these! Underline the subject and circle the active verb in each sentence.

a The dragon breathed fire and smoke.

b The tennis player hit the ball.

c The princess married the prince.

d Sam won first prize in the raffle.

e The squirrel climbed the tree.

f Some rabbits live in burrows.

g The farmer ploughed the field.

h Dr Jones visited Mrs Hills.

Task 2 Super! Now think of a suitable active verb to complete each sentence.

a St George _____ a dragon.

b Arsenal _____ Liverpool 2–1.

c Emma _____ on the computer.

d I _____ the soup all over my lap.

e The Normans _____ Britain.

f The bully _____ the small boy.

g The lady _____ me my change.

h I _____ at the strange sight.

10

Task 3 Practice makes perfect! Match up the active and passive forms of each sentence.

Active form	Passive form
a The cat chased the mouse.	A bag was carried by the lady.
b The squirrel hid the nuts.	A book was read by Pointy.
c The lady carried a bag.	The mouse was chased by the cat.
d Pointy read a book.	Hats are worn by all wizards.
e All wizards wear hats.	The nuts were hidden by the squirrel.

Task 4 You are getting on well! Super! Now change these sentences from the active to the passive.

a The spider spun a web. 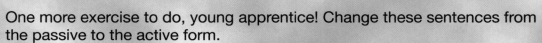 _A web was spun by the spider._

b Edward won first prize. _____

c The mother read a story. _____

d Shirin drew a nice picture. _____

e The farmer chased the boy. _____

Sorcerer's Skill Check

One more exercise to do, young apprentice! Change these sentences from the passive to the active form.

a The bread was nibbled by mice. _Mice nibbled the bread._

b The bus was driven by a woman. _____

c A carrot was eaten by the horse. _____

d The coin was picked up by the boy. _____

e The seeds were planted by Harry. _____

Slurp ... give yourself a gold star! You're getting on so well.
You'll be as bright as us, soon!

Clasping Clauses

Oops! I'm here to tell you about clauses, but I'm not absolutely sure about them myself! I believe that a clause is a group of words with a verb that makes sense on its own. A clause can be used as a whole sentence or as part of a sentence.

A simple one-clause sentence always has two parts:

the subject – that is who or what the sentence is about

the predicate – that is the rest of the sentence.

The wizard (was holding a test tube).

subject   (predicate)

Task 1 Oh dear! I need your help! Can you join up each subject with a suitable predicate for me?

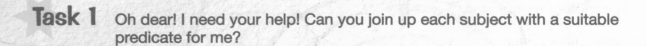

a	The spider	went to bed early.
b	Uncle Ben	was very untidy.
c	The tired boy	made a web.
d	Some brave mountaineers	shone very brightly.
e	My handwriting	skidded on some oil.
f	The sun	came to visit me.
g	The sports car	turned brown.
h	The leaves	reached the summit.

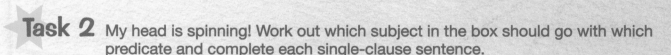

Task 2
My head is spinning! Work out which subject in the box should go with which predicate and complete each single-clause sentence.

A fork of lightning	Submarines	The greedy girl	A band
The apple	The clown	Swallows	The explorers

a _____ marched past.

b _____ ate a huge cake.

c _____ wore baggy trousers.

d _____ migrate in autumn.

e _____ flashed in the sky.

f _____ can go under the sea.

g _____ studied the map.

h _____ was rotten.

Task 3
Abracadada! Oh no! I need your help again! Underline the subject and circle the verb in each one-clause sentence.

a Volcanoes sometimes erupt.

b The ships bobbed up and down.

c My sister and I had a row.

d The girl rode her bike in the park.

e The wind howled through the trees.

f I dropped my cup of tea.

g Ben ate a large stick of rock.

h The children entered the museum.

Sorcerer's Skill Check

Phew! Thank goodness! We've nearly finished! Think of a suitable predicate to go with each subject to complete each single-clause sentence.

a The scary monster _____.

b My family _____.

c Some sheep _____.

d The wild wind _____.

e Curry _____.

You have coped very well, my apprentice.
You deserve a gold star for your perseverance.

Apprentice Wizard Challenge 1

Challenge 1 Rewrite each sentence in standard English.

a The frogs was very muddy. _____

b Who's got me book? _____

c It ain't fair! _____

d I 'ad a bike for me birthday. _____

e She don't work very hard. _____

f He didn't do nothing. _____

Challenge 2 Choose the best word to replace each longer phrase.

slyly	sadly	silently	difficult	agony	suddenly	hungry

a The cat crawled (<u>without any noise</u>) _____.

b The woman was in (<u>great pain</u>) _____.

c John left home (<u>with sadness</u>) _____.

d The test was (<u>not very easy</u>) _____.

e (<u>All at once</u>) _____ there was a loud noise.

f The dog was (<u>in need of food</u>) _____.

g The boy answered (<u>in a sly manner</u>) _____.

Challenge 3 Rewrite each sentence in indirect speech.

a "May I come with you?" Edward asked his mum.

_____

b "You can't, because I'm going into town," his mum replied.

_____

c "It's not fair!" shouted Edward crossly.

_____

Challenge 4 Choose the correct word to complete each common expression.

tongue	mouth	belt	way	meet
teacup	cat	cart	tree	fence

a to let the _____ out of the bag

b a storm in a _____

c barking up the wrong _____

d sitting on the _____

e making both ends _____

f to get your own _____

g on the tip of my _____

h to hit below the _____

i to put the _____ before the horse

j to live from hand to _____

Challenge 5 Complete each sentence with a suitable passive verb.

a The picnic was _____ by Mugly and Bugly.

b The bridge was _____ by the car.

c Many books were _____ by Roald Dahl.

d The house was _____ by the burglar.

e The palace was _____ by soldiers.

f The can of beans was _____ by Mr Griggs.

g The long dress was _____ by the beautiful actress.

h The goal was _____ by the winger.

Challenge 6 Underline the subject and circle the verb in each single-clause sentence.

a Marvellous Mr Magoo did some amazing conjuring tricks.

b The circus came to town.

c Some silly clowns fell over each other.

d A group of young acrobats entertained us.

e The muscular strongman bent iron bars with his teeth.

Place another gold star on your certificate! Super!

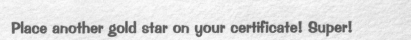

Two-Clause Sentences

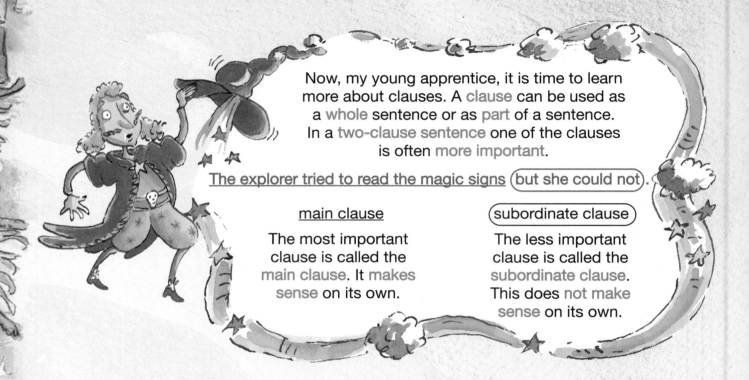

Now, my young apprentice, it is time to learn more about clauses. A clause can be used as a whole sentence or as part of a sentence. In a two-clause sentence one of the clauses is often more important.

The explorer tried to read the magic signs (but she could not).

main clause

The most important clause is called the main clause. It makes sense on its own.

(subordinate clause)

The less important clause is called the subordinate clause. This does not make sense on its own.

★ **Task 1**   Now have a go at this exercise. Hey presto! Underline the main clause in each sentence. Circle the subordinate clause.

a   The wizard stirred the cauldron as he made a magic potion.

b   Tom tried hard at maths and only got one sum wrong.

c   The dog looked fierce but it was really quite friendly.

d   The teacher saw Sam and smiled at her.

e   The snow fell heavily and blocked the main road.

f   We went out in the rain and got soaked.

g   Our teacher was angry with us because we talked too much.

h   My nose is red because I have a bad cold.

i   I visited Greece where I saw many interesting things.

j   Children are not allowed in unless they are with an adult.

k   The flowers did not grow although I watered them.

Task 2
See if you can work your magic in this exercise. Match up each main clause with a sensible subordinate clause to make a two-clause sentence.

Main clauses	Subordinate clauses
a You can't come in	when we visited the safari park.
b It often rains in winter	after it had been fed.
c We saw many lions	when Pointy stroked it.
d The cat purred	so I always carry an umbrella.
e The baby went to sleep	unless you promise to behave.

Task 3
You are doing well! After each sentence write if it is a simple sentence  with one clause, or a complex sentence with two clauses.

a Mugly and Bugly snored loudly. **S**

b The boys got on their bikes and cycled to the park.

c The strong man lifted the rock.

d Tara shut the door but left the window open.

e Our mum shouted when we made a lot of noise.

f I drank some water.

Sorcerer's Skill Check

Think of a suitable second clause to finish each sentence. Allakazan!

a I found the key which _____.

b The old boat sank because _____.

c Emma began to limp badly after _____.

d I know a man who _____.

Oops! My word, you've managed to do very well, I think! Stick a gold star on your certificate.

Perplexing Punctuation

Croak! We just want to tell you about the importance of punctuation before we have a snooze! Punctuation marks help the reader understand the meaning better. Punctuation marks can make a lot of difference!

PRIVATE.
NO SPELLS ALLOWED.

PRIVATE? NO!
SPELLS ALLOWED.

Task 1   Slurp ... if you can spare the time, put in the missing full stops, commas, question marks and exclamation marks in these sentences!

a   We were playing in their bedroom making a nasty mess

b   At the shop Mary bought a cabbage a bag of potatoes and a turnip

c   Have you seen Smudge my dog

d   I absolutely HATE custard

e   Mrs Barnes drove her car the red sporty one to town

f   Did you know that gorillas are found in Africa

g   Do you like Manchester United I do

h   What a lovely surprise

i   Peter do you prefer pizza or spaghetti

j   Last year we went to Greece Turkey Italy and France

k   Yuk I think sprouts are awful

Task 2

In these sentences all the commas, apostrophes and speech marks have been left out. Put them in for us while we have some lunch. (Where should the apostrophe go in **c** and **e**?)

a The old troll all wrinkled and ugly lived under the bridge.

b Come here Dan James said.

c The child whispered Lets get out of here!

d Tom who looked very scared ran to the door and shouted Catch me if you can!

e After a while Sam appeared and said Its time for dinner.

Task 3

Brain cell alert! Copy and punctuate each sentence correctly.

a wizard whimstaff asked would you like to help me miss snufflebeam

_____

b bring me my book pencils crayons and ruler jack david said

_____

c sam asked how far is it to the houses of parliament

_____

Sorcerer's Skill Check

This is a job for Pointy – or can you manage it? Match up the correct definition with the name of each punctuation mark.

a	Full stops	show when a question is being asked.
b	Commas	enclose information and keep it separate.
c	Question marks	come at the end of sentences.
d	Exclamation marks	show possession and when letters are missing.
e	Speech marks	show that something is being said with feeling.
f	Apostrophes	enclose what a person says.
g	Brackets	show you when to pause, before you carry on.

Super effort, young apprentice! You certainly deserve a gold star!

Gruesome Gender

Listen carefully, while I explain about gender. Nouns may be feminine, masculine, common or neuter.

girl

This is a feminine (female) noun.

boy

This is a masculine (male) noun.

teacher

This is a common noun. It could refer to a male or a female.

school

This is a neuter noun. Neuter means it has no gender.

Task 1 Abracadabra! Try this, my apprentice! Match up these masculine and feminine nouns.

Masculine	Feminine		Write them here.
king	mother	a	_____
brother	niece	b	_____
father	queen	c	_king_ _____ _queen_
man	aunt	d	_____
husband	woman	e	_____
nephew	wife	f	_____
uncle	sister	g	_____
bridegroom	girl	h	_____
prince	lady	i	_____
lord	princess	j	_____
boy	bride	k	_____

Task 2

Do the best you can with this exercise! Rewrite these sentences. Change all the masculine nouns into feminine.

a   The lion roared loudly.   *The lioness roared loudly.*

b   The bridegroom is my nephew.   _____

c   The old man is a widower.   _____

d   The king spoke to the prince.   _____

e   The father gave his son a present. _____

Task 3

Write each noun on the scroll in the correct column. Hey presto!

| monk | tree | bachelor | child | doctor | television | widower | cup |
| aunt | father | bride | widow | tooth | caretaker | sister | friend |

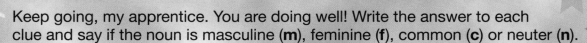

Masculine	Feminine	Common	Neuter

Sorcerer's Skill Check

Keep going, my apprentice. You are doing well! Write the answer to each clue and say if the noun is masculine (**m**), feminine (**f**), common (**c**) or neuter (**n**).

a   _____swamp_____   wet, marshy, low-lying ground   *n*

b   _____   the main female character in a book ⭐

c   _____   a child whose parents are dead ⭐

d   _____   a man or boy who has done a brave deed ⭐

Brain cell alert! Your brain must be red-hot!
Get yourself a gold star and cool off!

Relative Pronouns

Relative pronouns are relatively
easy when you know how!
They take the place of nouns and sometimes act
as conjunctions, joining two sentences together.

We always use who for people.
We can use either which or that for animals, places and things.

Wizard Whimstaff is a wise man. Wizard Whimstaff likes reading.
Wizard Whimstaff is a wise man <u>who</u> likes reading.

Pointy caught a spider. The spider was hairy.
Pointy caught a spider <u>which</u> was hairy.

Task 1 You'll soon get the hang of it! Choose **who** or **which** to complete
each sentence. Super!

a I opened the door _____ creaked loudly.

b I tried to see out of the window _____ was dirty.

c Wizard Whimstaff is my favourite teacher _____ teaches me about magic.

d I picked up my bag _____ was full of books.

e I hung up the picture _____ had fallen down.

f The policeman caught the thief _____ tried to run away.

g I talked to the boy _____ was nearest to me.

h I thanked the lady _____ helped me.

Task 2 Now have a try at these! Rewrite these sentences. Use **who** or **which** to join them. Practice makes perfect!

a The wizard thanked Mugly and Bugly. They gave him a present.

The wizard thanked Mugly and Bugly, who gave him a present.

b My mum cleaned the room. It was very dusty.

_____

c The man sat on the wooden bench. It was not very comfortable.

_____

d Tom was smaller than Sam. She was older than him.

_____

Task 3 Rewrite the sentences in a similar way to the example, using **who** or **which**.

Take care with the sentences. Notice how the commas are used in the example.

a The girl spoke to the boy. She was wearing her new jeans.

The girl, who was wearing her new jeans, spoke to the boy.

b The old man could not hear the music. He was a little deaf.

_____

c The cakes were burnt. Alfred baked them.

_____

d The dog greedily ate up all its dinner. The dog was very hungry.

_____

Sorcerer's Skill Check

One more to do! Super! Use **who** or **which** to complete these sentences.

a I opened the bottle in _____ there was a strange potion.

b The lady _____ sat near me wore a big hat.

c I did not like the shirt _____ Mum bought for me.

d No one believed the story _____ Sam told.

My young apprentice, you have excelled yourself! Accept a gold star!

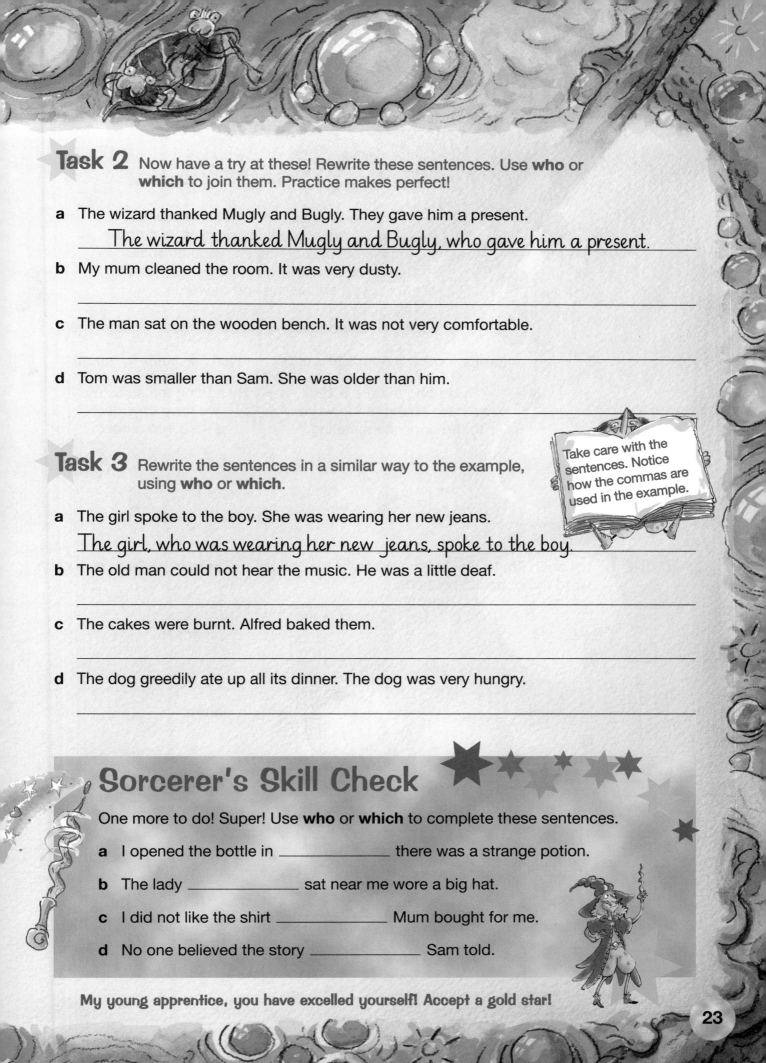

Terrible Transformations

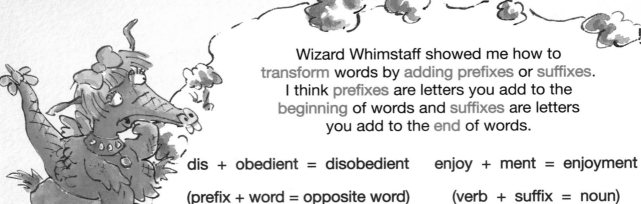

Wizard Whimstaff showed me how to transform words by adding prefixes or suffixes. I think prefixes are letters you add to the beginning of words and suffixes are letters you add to the end of words.

dis + obedient = disobedient

(prefix + word = opposite word)

By adding the prefix dis we have changed the word to the opposite meaning.

enjoy + ment = enjoyment

(verb + suffix = noun)

By adding the suffix ment we have changed a verb into a noun.

Task 1 Oh dear! I'm terribly confused. Help me choose the correct prefix to give each word the opposite meaning.

a un / dis → _un_ safe

b ig / il ____legible

c dis / mis ____appear

d im / in ____patient

e in / non ____sense

f non / mis ____behave

g im / in ____correct

h ir / il ____regular

i ig / ab ____noble

j un / ab ____normal

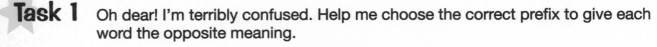

24

Task 2
Oops! All this thinking makes my head spin! Help me add suffixes from the box to change the verbs into nouns.

Take care! Sometimes the spelling of the original word does not remain exactly the same when you add the suffix. Use a dictionary if you are not sure.

ment	sion	ure	ance	al	tion

a invade   _invasion_

b move   _____

c assist   _____

d attract   _____

e arrive   _____

f seize   _____

g revive   _____

h advertise   _____

i televise   _____

j please   _____

k resemble   _____

l create   _____

Task 3
I think I'm seeing stars! Match up each abstract noun with the adjective from which it comes.

honest   strong   hateful   anger   hatred   pleasure

ugly   pleasing   angry   strength   ugliness   honesty

Sorcerer's Skill Check

Help me think of words beginning with each of these prefixes.

a de_____   **b** sub_____   **c** com_____   **d** pre_____

Cabradababa! Now help me think of words ending with each of these suffixes.

e _____en   **f** _____ish   **g** _____ery   **h** _____hood

Super! Add a gold star to your certificate, young apprentice!

25

Chilling Changes

Let me show you how we can experiment with this sentence. Super!

Miss Snufflebeam raced into the cave.

1 We can shorten it.
She raced into it.

2 We can change the order of the words.
Into the cave raced Miss Snufflebeam.

3 We can lengthen the sentence.
In a cloud of dust, an agitated
Miss Snufflebeam raced into the cave.

Task 1 You'll soon get the hang of these! Shorten these sentences. Leave out the adjectives and change the nouns into pronouns.

a The noisy frogs croaked in the dense green forest.   _They croaked in it._

b The greedy boy ate the deep pan pepperoni pizza.   _____

c The fierce sharks basked in the warm water.   _____

d Emma and I packed the brown case.   _____

e Sam gave the burger to her brother.   _____

Task 2 Now try this. Shorten each sentence by crossing out all the adjectives and adverbs

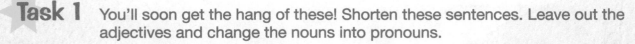

a The kind, clever wizard chanted softly.

b The handsome prince jumped quickly on to his white horse.

c Suddenly the speeding car raced past the shop.

d The old, grey elephant lumbered slowly along the overgrown path.

e Some huge, black clouds gathered menacingly in the sky.

f The attractive actress smiled sweetly at the photographers.

Task 3 Miss Snufflebeam has written some sentences, but got some words in the wrong order. Move around the words in each sentence to help it make sense.

a The book was written in the spell. _The spell was written in the book._

b The fire breathed dragon. _____

c The mouse has caught a cat. _____

d The hair washed her girl. _____

e A dragon is tiny but an ant is huge. _____

f The shirt was wearing a boy. _____

Task 4 Add as many words, phrases or clauses as you like to make these sentences more interesting. Practice makes perfect!

a The bats flew into the cave. _____
_____

b The wind was blowing. _____
_____

c A spacecraft landed. _____
_____

Sorcerer's Skill Check

Super! A final task for you. Make these pairs of sentences more interesting by making them into one sentence as shown.

a The snake hissed loudly. It slithered through the grass.
   Hissing loudly, the snake slithered through the grass.

b The old lady picked up her umbrella. She went out into the rain.
   _____

c The motorist drove quickly. He arrived in good time.
   _____

Rabracadada! You have done your tasks so well, you deserve another gold star!

Apprentice Wizard Challenge 2

Challenge 1 Think of a suitable subordinate clause to finish off each sentence.

a I chanted the spell but _____.

b The apple fell from the tree and _____.

c My mum hung out the washing because _____.

d I switched off the computer when _____.

e The train stopped at the station although _____.

f You can't leave until _____.

g Sam spoke to the old lady who _____.

Challenge 2 Punctuate the sentences with the missing punctuation marks shown.

a Have you seen my hat   (question mark)

b I hate the rain   (exclamation mark)

c Mr Smith our neighbour is friendly.   (two commas)

d When I m ready, I ll go home.   (two apostrophes)

e Mrs Shah said "Please help me."   (one comma)

f I can do it, Sam said.   (speech marks)

g Roald Dahl a writer wrote many books.   (pair of brackets)

h Mary s bag was under the chair.   (apostrophe)

Challenge 3 After each noun write if it is masculine ⭐m, feminine ⭐f, common ⭐c or neuter ⭐n.

a nun ⭐   **d** child ⭐   **g** tap ⭐   **j** doctor ⭐

b teacher ⭐   **e** television ⭐   **h** monk ⭐   **k** friend ⭐

c hat ⭐   **f** policewoman ⭐   **i** widower ⭐   **l** countess ⭐

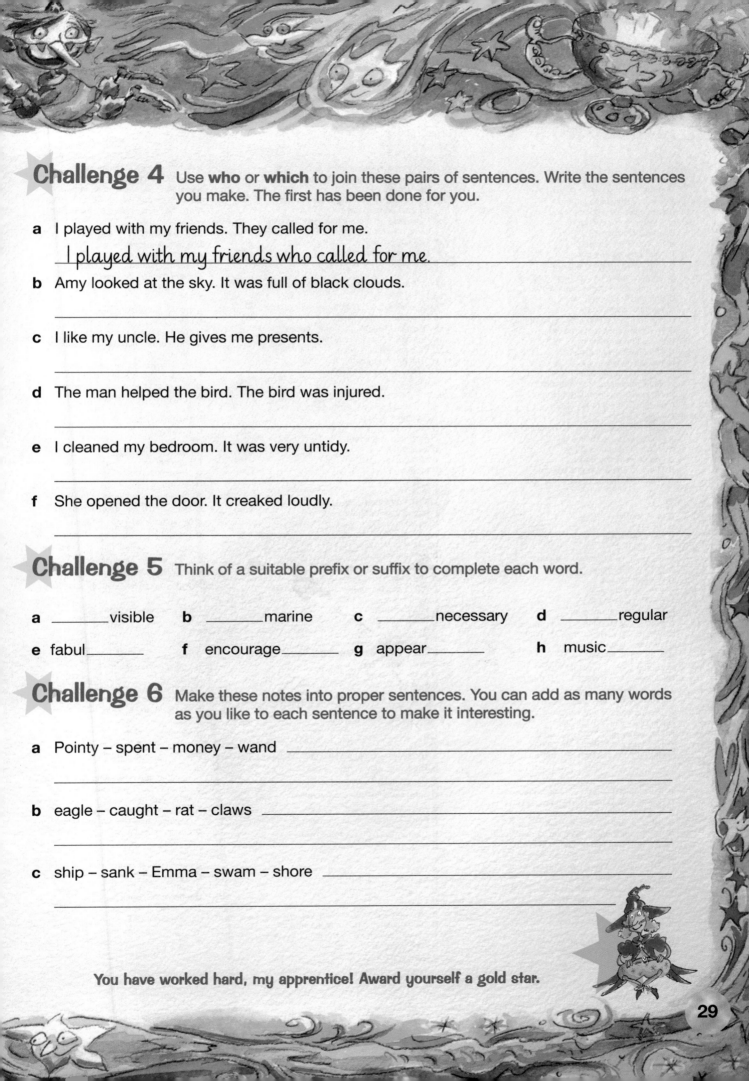

Challenge 4
Use **who** or **which** to join these pairs of sentences. Write the sentences you make. The first has been done for you.

a I played with my friends. They called for me.

I played with my friends who called for me.

b Amy looked at the sky. It was full of black clouds.

_____

c I like my uncle. He gives me presents.

_____

d The man helped the bird. The bird was injured.

_____

e I cleaned my bedroom. It was very untidy.

_____

f She opened the door. It creaked loudly.

_____

Challenge 5
Think of a suitable prefix or suffix to complete each word.

a _____visible **b** _____marine **c** _____necessary **d** _____regular

e fabul_____ **f** encourage_____ **g** appear_____ **h** music_____

Challenge 6
Make these notes into proper sentences. You can add as many words as you like to each sentence to make it interesting.

a Pointy – spent – money – wand _____

_____

b eagle – caught – rat – claws _____

_____

c ship – sank – Emma – swam – shore _____

_____

You have worked hard, my apprentice! Award yourself a gold star.

Answers

Pages 2–3

Task 1 Standard English – f, g, h, i, j
Non-standard English – a, b, c, d, e

Task 2
a I could easily have eaten it.
b I am more sensible than you.
c These are not my boots.
d We saw him do it.
e Do you want a sweet?
f All of us were hungry.
g I don't know anything about it.

Task 3 Suggested answers, as these may vary.
a He taught me some magic tricks.
b Dan and I hid in the cellar.
c I am not going out.
d We were just stirring the cauldron.
e That's the spell that I made up.
f We are coming soon.
g What have you got there?
h You did it well.
i He should have taken more care.
j Have you seen my broomstick?
k We were lucky not to get caught.
l Give me one of those apples.

Sorcerer's Skill Check
Suggested answers, as these may vary.
a I'm never doing tricks again!
b I haven't got any money.
c I don't want any trouble.
d They weren't anywhere near me.
e The children did not take any notice.

Pages 4–5

Task 1
a Mr – Mister
b Rd – Road
c NB – note well
d St – Saint
e USA – United States of America
f GB – Great Britain
g PS – postscript
h etc. – and so on
i RSVP – please reply
j PTO – please turn over

Task 2
a trees   e clothing   i sports
b cereals   f capital cities j insects
c animals   g tools
d fish   h metals

Task 3
a abbreviation c chorus   e ewe
b beaker   d desert   f fountain

Sorcerer's Skill Check
Suggested answers, as these may vary.
a The damp cave was underground.
b Her older sister helped her.
c The thirsty girl asked for a drink.
d The heavy rain flooded the street.
e Her bright red dress was smart.

Pages 6–7

Task 1
a The magician chanted, "Abracadabra!"
b Kyle asked, "What is the answer?"
c "Let's go out to play," suggested Paul.
d "Stop shouting!" the teacher ordered.
e "I like your trainers," William sighed.
f "It's raining outside," Shannon said.
g "Tell me a story," the toddler pleaded.
h "I don't like custard!" Amy exclaimed.

Task 2
a "I can hop," the frog said.
b The girl boasted, "I'm the best at spelling."
c Dionne complained, "I feel worn out."
d "What are you looking at?" James asked.
e Cara shouted, "Stop it!"
f "Have you seen my pen?" Ben asked.
g The lady snapped, "Get out of my way!"

Task 3 Suggested answers, as these may vary.
a The wizard said that he had just got a new cloak.
b Mr Parish told his neighbour that his car had broken down.
c Harry told his mum that he would really like a bike for his birthday.
d The teacher asked Cara if she had done her homework.
e Mrs Dodds ordered Sarah to stop shouting.
f Mr Parsons shouted at Ben to go away.

Sorcerer's Skill Check
Suggested answers, as these may vary.
a "I'm tired," Mugly said.
b "How are you, Hugh?" Mary asked.
c Amy said, "I've lost my bag."
d Paul said, "I can swim."
e "The path is muddy," Tom said.
f "May I go home?" Ben asked.

Pages 8–9

Task 1 Suggested answers, as these may vary.
a alive and kicking
b fame and fortune
c head and shoulders
d lock and key
e stuff and nonsense
f tooth and nail
g safe and sound
h chop and change
i flesh and blood
j high and dry/mighty
k touch and go
l here and now
m ways and means
n over and above

Task 2
a A new broom sweeps clean.
b The early bird catches the worm.
c A fool and his money are soon parted.
d No news is good news.
e Practice makes perfect.
f Still waters run deep.
g One good turn deserves another.

Task 3
a All's well that ends well.
b Fair exchange is no robbery.
c Once bitten, twice shy.
d Better late than never.
e First come, first served.
f Great minds think alike.

Sorcerer's Skill Check
Many answers are possible.

Pages 10–11

Task 1
a The dragon (breathed) fire and smoke.
b The tennis player (hit) the ball.
c The princess (married) the prince.
d Sam (won) first prize in the raffle.
e The squirrel (climbed) the tree.
f Some rabbits (live) in burrows.
g The farmer (ploughed) the field.
h Dr Jones (visited) Mrs Hills.

Task 2 Suggested answers, as these may vary.
a killed   e invaded
b beat   f hit
c turned   g gave
d spilt   h stared

Task 3
a The mouse was chased by the cat.
b The nuts were hidden by the squirrel.
c A bag was carried by the lady.
d A book was read by Pointy.
e Hats are worn by all wizards.

Task 4
a A web was spun by the spider.
b The first prize was won by Edward.
c A story was read by the mother.
d A nice picture was drawn by Shirin.
e The boy was chased by the farmer.

Sorcerer's Skill Check
a Mice nibbled the bread.
b A woman drove the bus.
c The horse ate a carrot.
d The boy picked up the coin.
e Harry planted the seeds.

Pages 12–13

Task 1
a The spider made a web.
b Uncle Ben came to visit me.
c The tired boy went to bed early.
d Some brave mountaineers reached the summit.
e My handwriting was very untidy.
f The sun shone very brightly.
g The sports car skidded on some oil.
h The leaves turned brown.

Task 2
a A band
b The greedy girl
c The clown
d Swallows
e A fork of lightning
f Submarines
g The explorers
h The apple

Task 3
a Volcanoes sometimes (erupt).
b The ships (bobbed) up and down.
c My sister and I (had) a row.
d The girl (rode) her bike in the park.
e The wind (howled) through the trees.
f I (dropped) my cup of tea.
g Ben (ate) a large stick of rock.
h The children (entered) the museum.

Sorcerer's Skill Check
Many answers are possible.

Pages 14–15

Challenge 1
a The frogs were very muddy.
b Who's got my book?
c It isn't fair!
d I had a bike for my birthday.
e She doesn't work very hard.
f He didn't do anything.

Challenge 2
a silently   d difficult   g slyly
b agony   e Suddenly
c sadly   f hungry

Challenge 3
Suggested answers, as these may vary.
a Edward asked his mum if he could come with her.
b His mum replied that he could not come because she was going into town.
c Edward shouted crossly that it was not fair.

Challenge 4
a cat   e meet   i cart
b teacup   f way   j mouth
c tree   g tongue
d fence   h belt

Challenge 5

Suggested answers, as these may vary.

a The picnic was eaten by Mugly and Bugly.
b The bridge was crossed by the car.
c Many books were written by Roald Dahl.
d The house was robbed by the burglar.
e The palace was attacked by soldiers.
f The can of beans was eaten by Mr Griggs.
g The long dress was worn by the beautiful actress.
h The goal was scored by the winger.

Challenge 6

a Marvellous Mr Magoo (did) some amazing conjuring tricks.
b The circus (came) to town.
c Some silly clowns (fell) over each other.
d A group of young acrobats (entertained) us.
e The muscular strongman (bent) iron bars with his teeth.

Pages 16–17

Task 1 **a** The wizard stirred the cauldron (as he made a magic potion).
b Tom tried hard at maths (and only got one sum wrong).
c The dog looked fierce (but it was really quite friendly).
d The teacher saw Sam (and smiled at her).
e The snow fell heavily (and blocked the main road).
f We went out in the rain (and got soaked).
g Our teacher was angry with us (because we talked too much).
h My nose is red (because I have a bad cold).
i I visited Greece (where I saw many interesting things).
j Children are not allowed in (unless they are with an adult).
k The flowers did not grow (although I watered them).

Task 2 **a** You can't come in unless you promise to behave.
b It often rains in winter so I always carry an umbrella.
c We saw many lions when we visited the safari park.
d The cat purred when Pointy stroked it.
e The baby went to sleep after it had been fed.

Task 3 **a** S **c** S **e** C
b C **d** C **f** S

Sorcerer's Skill Check
Many answers are possible.

Pages 18–19

Task 1 **a** We were playing in their bedroom, making a nasty mess.
b At the shop, Mary bought a cabbage, a bag of potatoes and a turnip.
c Have you seen Smudge, my dog?
d I absolutely HATE custard!
e Mrs Barnes drove her car, the red sporty one, to town.
f Did you know that gorillas are found in Africa?
g Do you like Manchester United? I do.
h What a lovely surprise!
i Peter, do you prefer pizza or spaghetti?
j Last year we went to Greece, Turkey, Italy and France.
k Yuk! I think sprouts are awful!

Task 2 **a** The old troll, all wrinkled and ugly, lived under the bridge.
b "Come here, Dan," James said.
c The child whispered, "Let's get out of here!"
d Tom, who looked very scared, ran to the door and shouted, "Catch me if you can!"
e After a while, Sam appeared and said, "It's time for dinner."

Task 3 **a** Wizard Whimstaff asked, "Would you like to help me, Miss Snufflebeam?"
b "Bring me my book, pencils, crayons and ruler, Jack," David said.
c Sam asked, "How far is it to the Houses of Parliament?"

Sorcerer's Skill Check
a Full stops come at the end of sentences.
b Commas show you when to pause, before you carry on.
c Question marks show when a question is being asked.
d Exclamation marks show that something is being said with feeling.
e Speech marks enclose what a person says.
f Apostrophes show possession and when letters are missing.
g Brackets enclose information and keep it separate.

Pages 20–21

Task 1 **a** father – mother
b nephew – niece
c king – queen
d uncle – aunt
e man – woman
f husband – wife
g brother – sister
h boy – girl
i lord – lady
j prince – princess
k bridegroom – bride

Task 2 **a** The lioness roared loudly.
b The bride is my niece.
c The old lady is a widow.
d The queen spoke to the princess.
e The mother gave her daughter a present.

Task 3 Masculine: monk, bachelor, widower, father
Feminine: aunt, bride, widow, sister
Common: child, doctor, caretaker, friend
Neuter: tree, television, cup, tooth

Sorcerer's Skill Check
a swamp (n) **c** orphan (c)
b heroine (f) **d** hero (m)

Pages 22–23

Task 1 **a** which **d** which **g** who
b which **e** which **h** who
c who **f** who

Task 2 **a** The wizard thanked Mugly and Bugly, who gave him a present.
b My mum cleaned the room, which was very dusty.
c The man sat on the wooden bench, which was not very comfortable.
d Tom was smaller than Sam, who was older than him.

Task 3 **a** The girl, who was wearing her new jeans, spoke to the boy.
b The old man, who was a little deaf, could not hear the music.
c The cakes, which Alfred baked, were burnt.
d The dog, which was very hungry, greedily ate up all its dinner.

Sorcerer's Skill Check
a which **c** which
b who **d** which

Pages 24–25

Task 1 **a** unsafe **f** misbehave
b illegible **g** incorrect
c disappear **h** irregular
d impatient **i** ignoble
e nonsense **j** abnormal

Task 2 **a** invasion **g** revival
b movement **h** advertisement
c assistance **i** television
d attraction **j** pleasure
e arrival **k** resemblance
f seizure **l** creation

Task 3 honest – honesty; strong – strength; hateful – hatred; ugly – ugliness; pleasing – pleasure; angry – anger

Sorcerer's Skill Check
Many answers are possible.

Pages 26–27

Task 1 **a** They croaked in it.
b He ate it.
c They basked in it.
d We packed it.
e She gave it to him.

Task 2 **a** The ~~kind~~, ~~clever~~ wizard chanted ~~softly~~.
b The ~~handsome~~ prince jumped ~~quickly~~ on to his ~~white~~ horse.
c ~~Suddenly~~ the ~~speeding~~ car raced past the shop.
d The ~~old~~, ~~grey~~ elephant lumbered ~~slowly~~ along the ~~overgrown~~ path.
e Some ~~huge~~, ~~black~~ clouds gathered ~~menacingly~~ in the sky.
f The ~~attractive~~ actress smiled ~~sweetly~~ at the photographers.

Task 3 **a** The spell was written in the book.
b The dragon breathed fire.
c The cat has caught a mouse.
d The girl washed her hair.
e A dragon is huge but an ant is tiny.
f The boy was wearing a shirt.

Task 4 Many answers are possible.

Sorcerer's Skill Check
a Hissing loudly, the snake slithered through the grass.
b Picking up her umbrella, the old lady went out into the rain.
c Driving quickly, the motorist arrived in good time.

Pages 28–29

Challenge 1
Many answers are possible.

Challenge 2
a Have you seen my hat?
b I hate the rain!
c Mr Smith, our neighbour, is friendly.
d When I'm ready I'll go home.
e Mrs Shah said, "Please help me."
f "I can do it," Sam said.
g Roald Dahl (a writer) wrote many books.
h Mary's bag was under the chair.

Challenge 3
a f **d** c **g** n **j** c
b c **e** n **h** m **k** c
c n **f** f **i** m **l** f

Challenge 4
a I played with my friends who called for me.
b Amy looked at the sky which was full of black clouds.
c I like my uncle who gives me presents.
d The man helped the bird which was injured.
e I cleaned my bedroom which was very untidy.
f She opened the door which creaked loudly.

Challenge 5
Suggested answers, as these may vary.
a invisible
b submarine
c unnecessary
d irregular
e fabulous
f encouragement
g appearance
h musical

Challenge 6
Many answers are possible.

31

Wizard's Certificate of Excellence

⭐ **Startling Standard English**

⭐ **Two-Clause Sentences**

⭐ **Spooky Summaries**

⭐ **Perplexing Punctuation**

⭐ **Sizzling Speech**

⭐ **Gruesome Gender**

⭐ **Common Expressions**

⭐ **Relative Pronouns**

⭐ **Active and Passive Verbs**

⭐ **Terrible Transformations**

⭐ **Clasping Clauses**

⭐ **Chilling Changes**

⭐ **Apprentice Wizard Challenge 1**

⭐ **Apprentice Wizard Challenge 2**

This is to state that Wizard Whimstaff awards

Apprentice _____

the title of English Wizard. Congratulations!

Wizard Whimstaff

Published 2002
10 9 8 7 6

Letts Educational, The Chiswick Centre,
414 Chiswick High Road, London W4 5TF
Tel: 0845 602 1937 Fax: 020 8742 8767
Email: mail@lettsed.co.uk
Website: www.Letts-SuccessZone.com

Text, design and illustrations © Letts Educational Ltd 2002

Author: Louis Fidge
Book Concept and Development:
Helen Jacobs, Publishing Director
Sophie London, Project Editor
Book Editor: Monica Kendall
Book Design: Linda Males
Illustrations: Mike Phillips and Neil Chapman
Cover Illustration: Neil Chapman

Letts Educational Limited, is a division of Granada Learning Limited.
Part of Granada plc.

British Library Cataloguing in Publication Data
A CIP record for this book is available from the British Library.

ISBN 1 84315 105 7

Printed in Italy

Colour reproduction by PDQ Digital Media Solutions Ltd. Bungay, Suffolk